FEATHERSTONE
Bloomsbury Publishing Plc
50 Bedford Square, London, WC1B 3DP, UK
29 Earlsfort Terrace, Dublin 2, Ireland

BLOOMSBURY, FEATHERSTONE and the Feather logo are trademarks of Bloomsbury Publishing Plc

First published in Great Britain 2019 by Bloomsbury Publishing Plc
Text copyright © Penny Tassoni, 2019
Illustrations copyright © Mel Four, 2019

Penny Tassoni and Mel Four have asserted their rights under the Copyright, Designs and Patents Act,
1988, to be identified as Author and Illustrator of this work

A catalogue record for this book is available from the British Library

ISBN: HB: 978-1-4729-6667-4; ePDF: 978-1-4729-6668-1; ePub: 978-1-4729-7433-4

4 6 8 10 9 7 5 3

Printed and bound in China by Leo Paper Products, Heshan, Guangdong

MIX
Paper from
responsible sources
FSC® C020056

FSC
www.fsc.org

To find out more about our authors and books visit www.bloomsbury.com and sign up for our newsletters

Time to Share

Penny Tassoni

Illustrated by Mel Four

FEATHERSTONE

LONDON   OXFORD   NEW YORK   NEW DELHI   SYDNEY

Everyone needs to share.

You can share to make things fair.

Before.

After.

You can share to show you care.

And to make friends too.

Sharing makes things more fun.

Before.

After.

There are places where you have to share like...

In the playground.

At the
swimming
pool.

At school
or nursery.

Which of these can you share?

Sand.

Trains.

Dough.

Dressing-up clothes.

Sometimes you have to ask to share.

'Can I come in?'

Sometimes others will ask you to share with them.

'Can I have one, please?'

Sometimes when you share you have to take turns.

Waiting can feel like a long time.

But try cheering along by...

Jumping up and down.

Singing a song.

Or doing a countdown.

Some things are not for sharing.

Do you
know why?

Sometimes special things are not for sharing.

Do you have anything special just for YOU?

Notes for parents and carers

Sharing is an important social skill. Children who can share and take turns find it easier to make friends. Sharing develops over time. By around three years old, most children can do some sharing independently for short periods of time. For sharing to develop, children need adult encouragement. There are many ways that you can help your child.

Helping your child to share

• Look out for opportunities to point out examples of sharing. This will give your child an understanding of what the word means.

• Role model sharing by passing things over to your child.

• Use meal times as a way of helping your child to learn to share, e.g. pass food to other people.

- Use play as a way of helping your child learn to share and take turns, e.g. sharing bricks, painting, rolling a ball back and forth.

- Praise your child if without prompting they offer to share something with you.

- Talk about how nice it feels when everyone can join in because things are being shared.

- Put out toys and objects that are easily shared when other children come around.

- Don't expect your child to share special things such as their comforters or favourite toys.

- Whilst you can remind your child that is nice to share, avoid forcing them to share.